The Biggest Bear Hunt

PIPPBROOK
BOOKS

It is the middle of the day.

Baby Bear is off playing in the sun
and Mummy Bear is feeling sleepy.

She sits down in front of a large grey
rock and in the blink of an eye,
she falls fast asleep.

A little while later she is woken by a sound.
"Buzz buzz buzz!" hums a busy bumblebee.

Mummy Bear rubs her eyes and looks around.
Where is Baby? He can't be found.

Mummy Bear
looks in the big
hollow tree,
but all she finds
is a puffy, fluffy owl.

Where, oh where, is Baby Bear?
He's giving Mummy such
a scare.

Mummy Bear looks behind the old log,
but all she finds is a dizzy, busy beaver.

Where, oh where, is Baby Bear?
He's disappeared into thin air.

Mummy Bear looks down by the river,
but all she finds is a splishy, splashy fish.

Where, oh where, is Baby Bear?
Now Mummy has looked everywhere!

Poor Mummy Bear.
She sits back down by the large
grey rock, and wonders what
to do next.

Just then she hears a noise:
a snuffling, snoring noise,
coming from behind the rock.

"Zzzzzzzzz!" it goes.

Mummy gets up and peeps around the rock.
Guess who she finds there, sound asleep?

There, oh there, is Baby Bear –
fast asleep without a care!